NUMERACY

Can-U-Cards

A creative approach to consolidating maths skills

PUBLISHING

BOOK 1

YEAR 1–3

Pauleen Novosel

Jason Novosel

Title:	Numeracy CAN U CARDS
	A creative approach to consolidating maths skills – Years 1–3: Book 1
Authors:	Pauleen Novosel and Jason Novosel
Editor:	Jennifer Clark
Designer:	Freshfields Graphic Design
Book code:	PB00105
ISBN:	978-1-908735-84-3
Published:	2012
Publisher:	TTS Group Ltd
	Park Lane Business Park
	Kirkby-in-Ashfield
	Notts, NG17 9GU
	Tel: 0800 318 686
	Fax: 0800 137 525
Websites:	www.tts-shopping.com
Copyright:	Text: © Bardroyal Books Pty Ltd, 2010
	Edition and illustrations: © TTS Group Ltd, 2012

About the authors: Pauleen Novosel has been teaching for more than 20 years in early childhood as well as being a music specialist, a relief teacher and a speech and drama teacher. Pauleen has taught in both private and state schools in Queensland, Australia, where she began her teaching career, as well as in the United Kingdom. With particular interests in literacy, early childhood and the arts, she has also been a guest speaker in literacy and has vast experience in curriculum planning and in the preparation and presentation of school-based documents for accreditation. Now enjoying her retirement, Pauleen continues her learning journey through travel and an interest in developing educational resources.

After beginning to teach in 1998 in a private secondary school in Queensland, Jason Novosel transitioned to the state secondary system as acting Head of Department English. Having gathered an array of teaching experiences and qualifications along the way, he has now launched his own training and consultancy business to pursue his passion for adult education. Jason has developed training and assessment units and has sat on district panels for curriculum subject development in Queensland. Jason shares his creative flair for designing educational materials with his mother and co-author, Pauleen.

Contents

Introduction

Can you imagine stepping off the *teach–test–record* train to enjoy a fulfilling learning interaction with your class? The *Numeracy CAN U CARDS* series offers just that opportunity with an informal, short and exploratory method of assessing basic numeracy skills. Created to complement the teaching of mathematical concepts such as number facts, place value and number operations, these fun (yet purposeful) CAN U CARDS invite all of your students to practise their numeracy skills in a supportive environment.

CAN U CARDS are structured developmentally in two platforms:

- Platform 1 (Years 1-3) is designed for the needs of children through to Year 3.
- Platform 2 (Years 4-6) spans Years 4–6.

These cards can also be useful in secondary education, adult numeracy classes and for teaching English to speakers of other languages. Although a sample set of CAN U questions is supplied with each card for convenience, you also have the option of creating your own questions to shape the learning experience to the specific needs of your group of learners.

The self-explanatory, simple design of CAN U CARDS is a great strength for classroom use. Although they cover an expanse of opportunities for learning, practice and the development of mental acuity, they do not require onerous preparation or an extensive system of pre-testing and matching of cards with students. They also bring with them a relaxed creativity and explorative camaraderie, changing the mood of any classroom and introducing an easy flow of dialogue, ideas and opinions while still focusing on the essential elements of numeracy.

So sit back and relax with a CAN U CARD and let the numeracy practice begin.

Curriculum links

Given the generic nature of the numeracy skills, the cards are relevant to a broad range of learners. In terms of specific curriculum fit, CAN U CARDS are designed for:

- the number and algebra content of the United Kingdom curriculum, aligning to the *Primary Framework for Literacy and Mathematics, September 2006*
- the number and algebra content of the Australian curriculum, aligning to the 2010 draft standards of the Australian curriculum
- the number and algebra content of the New Zealand curriculum, aligning to the *New Zealand Curriculum 2007*.

What will students learn from Platform 1?

By the time they have completed Platform 1, students will have:

- practised place value to 1 000
- recognised the number parts and the size of simple fractions, for example ¼, ½
- identified number patterns including multiples of 2, 5 and 10
- understood comparative mathematical language used to describe numbers.

The chart outlines the specific learning objectives for each colour of the cards.

Mathematics concept	Green	Yellow	Red
Counting	Count 0–20 and then beyond to 100. Count by twos, fives, tens starting from 0.	Count number sequences increasing by ones, twos, fives, tens from any starting point up to 100.	Count number sequences increasing and decreasing by ones, twos, fives, tens from any starting point.
Numeration	Match number names, numerals and quantities to 10. Recognise, represent and order numbers to 100. Subitise and partition numbers.	Recognise, represent, write and order numbers to 130. Subitise and partition numbers.	Recognise, represent, visualise, write and order numbers to 1 000 and beyond.
Comparative language	Compare and order collections to 20 and beyond, using *more*, *less* and *same*.	Compare and order collections to 20 and beyond, using *larger*, *smaller*, *most*, *least* and *equal*.	Compare and order collections beyond 20, using *greater than* and *less than*.
Place value	Count collections to 100 by grouping in tens. Count in tens and then use partitioning to regroup those numbers (10 + 10 + 10 = 30).	Work with larger collections to 1 000 by grouping in hundreds and tens. Count the tens and hundreds and use place value to partition and regroup those numbers.	Use hundreds, tens and ones to partition and regroup numbers to 1 000.
Fractions	Understand one-half as one of two equal parts. Recognise halves of collections.	Recognise and use halves, quarters and thirds of everyday shapes, objects and collections.	Recognise fractions as equal parts of regular shapes, collections or numbers. Connect number of parts with the fraction size.
Addition and subtraction	Represent and solve additive situations involving combining and counting on.	Represent and solve additive situations involving combining, changing or identifying missing elements of a number.	Solve additive situations involving mental strategies for addition and subtraction.
Multiplication and division		Represent and solve simple multiplicative situations including *groups of*, *arrays* and *sharing*.	Solve multiplicative situations including *for each* and *times as many* using mental strategies.
Number patterns	Sort and classify objects. Copy, continue, create and describe patterns with objects and numbers to 100.	Copy, continue, create describe and identify missing elements of place value patterns.	Copy, continue, create and describe place value patterns including patterns resulting from performing a single operation.

Source: Adapted from Draft Australian Curriculum 2010

Why is numeracy so important?

Numeracy, along with literacy, provides the basics of any classroom education. Every subject area draws on these skills – even if it simply involves locating a page in a sequence of numbers. A pertinent illustration of the practical relevance of "getting the basics right" is the constant complaint from employers that they cannot find employees who are competent in spelling, vocabulary and sentence construction or who can function without a calculator.

During our careers in education (between us spanning a period of more than 50 years), we have been trained in, exposed to and engaged with a wide variety of learning methodologies for teaching the basics – from the traditionalist rote method of the mid 20th century to the pedagogies supporting theories of multiple intelligences and self-directed learning. Certainly we recognise that learning and teaching styles are fluid and influenced by society's current understanding of cognition and development – and we have practised the teaching strategies associated with modern educational psychology. At the same time, across the years it remains fundamental that learners need to master the basic knowledge of numbers (and words) before they can achieve self-actualisation in learning.[1]

CAN U CARDS therefore move learners towards more creative uses of mathematics by first offering them strong extrinsic motivation for learning numeracy in its basic forms. In essence, these cards inject diversity, enjoyment and collegial interaction into purposeful learning and practice activities that focus on mental acuity rather than drill.

10 good reasons to use CAN U CARDS

CAN U CARDS provide great opportunities to:

1. **practise** concepts as they occur in real life – randomly, not drilled and predictable

2. **discuss** concepts taught in previous lessons

3. **identify** mathematical exceptions

4. **use** minimal equipment in valuable learning experiences (individual whiteboards, class board and a calculator)

5. **promote** authentic mental acuity for all students

6. **adapt** information to suit the needs of your students

7. **acknowledge** extension students

8. **encourage** reluctant learners

9. **share** knowledge with valuable teacher and student interaction

10. **challenge** participants.

---

1 Abraham Maslow (1943) A theory of human motivation. *Psychological Review*, 50: 370–96; Theory into Practice, Conditions of learning (R Gagne), http://tip.psychology.org/gagne.html, accessed 24 February 2010.

How do I use the CAN U Cards?

In this book, Platform 1 CAN U CARDS are divided into three different colours: green (six cards), yellow (eight cards) and red (eight cards). Each card is accompanied by a sample set of questions. Within this broad structure there is considerable versatility:

- As students move along from green to yellow to red, the mathematical content becomes more difficult. Within a certain colour, however, the card number does not reflect that same developmental progression. For example, Green Card 6 is easier than Yellow Card 1, but Red Card 5 isn't necessarily more difficult than Red Card 3. Within a colour, therefore, you may choose an order that suits the needs of your students and classroom programme.

- CAN U CARDS also lend themselves to differentiated classroom instruction. You can use CAN U CARDS as a whole class activity or with small groups, pairs and individuals. Depending on the abilities of your students, you may need to facilitate the discussions during the CAN U CARD sessions.

- CAN U CARDS have the versatility to be used either orally as mental exercises or in written form. If working with individual whiteboards, students can display a record of their thinking that the whole class or group can reflect on later.

- Activities are not limited to the sample CAN U questions provided. With the CAN U CARDS as a springboard, you can create your own questions designed with the specific needs of your group of learners in mind.

Just follow the simple preparations and teaching instructions on the next page and then let the numeracy CAN U CARD journey begin.

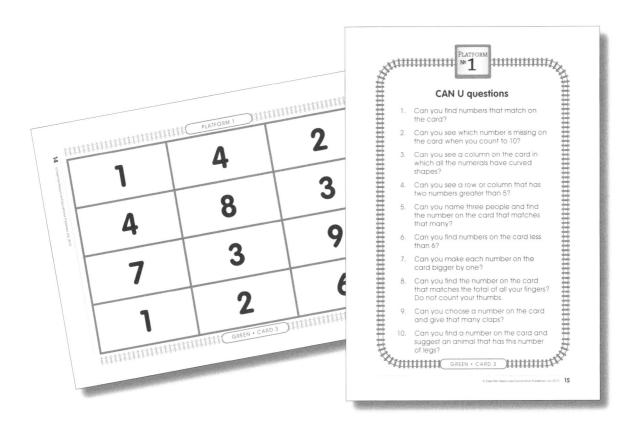

Preparing the CAN U CARDS

Note: These instructions apply only if you plan to use the cards with small groups, pairs or individuals. If you plan to practise these cards with the whole class, move straight to "Teaching with the CAN U CARDS". If you are preparing cards, we also recommend – in recognition of the many demands teachers have on their time – that you recruit parent volunteers or teaching assistants / teacher aides to help you with this stage.

1. If coloured copy paper is available, photocopy the CAN U CARDS on green, yellow and red paper. If coloured copy paper is not available, photocopy the CAN U CARDS on white paper and highlight or underline the card number with the designated colour. The number of copies you need to make of each card will depend on how you intend to use the cards.

2. Laminate the photocopied cards or use sheet protectors to make them more durable.

3. If you are using the "CAN U questions" sheets, photocopy as many copies as you need on white copy paper.

4. Laminate the photocopied question sheets or use sheet protectors to make them more durable.

5. If students are to record their answers on the recording sheet template (p 59), photocopy as many copies as you need on white copy paper.

Teaching with the CAN U CARDS

Note: It is assumed that students have learnt the relevant numeracy concepts set out in the curriculum before they work with a CAN U CARD.

1. If you want the **whole class** to use the same card and set of questions, copy the CAN U CARD grid on a whiteboard, electronic whiteboard or overhead projector. Read the questions aloud to the students for them to answer (on individual whiteboards, orally, or in writing on the recording sheet template or in their notebooks).

2. If you want **small groups**, **pairs** or **individuals** to use different cards and sets of questions, prepare the cards as described above and then pass out the cards, questions and recording sheets (if you are using them). Students then record their answers on the recording sheet template or in their notebook.

3. For **reluctant learners**, ask them to complete only a select number of questions, and don't impose a time limit. Regularly review and revisit the cards to help consolidate learning throughout the year. Over time you may also find these learners gain confidence to actively contribute as they observe the open-endedness and diversity of answers.

4. For **extension students**, ask them to complete all of the questions in a certain amount of time. Challenge them to modify the CAN U CARDS to make them more difficult or give them copies of the CAN U CARD template to create new cards and questions for other classmates to solve. Also, If you have Book 2 of the series, you may use cards and questions from Platform 2, which are designed for higher year levels.

10 hints for working with CAN U CARDS

1. Card numbers within a colour set (green, yellow or red) do not reflect a developmental progression.

2. Revision and consolidation of concepts are inbuilt.

3. The design of multiple answers on each card allows learners to experience success, whether they provide a basic response or a more creative one.

4. Oral questioning facilitates the development of listening skills.

5. You may find it useful to break questions into parts according to the needs of your students.

6. The cards lend themselves to interactive e-learning sessions, in which information and communication technology (ICT) becomes integral to learning.

7. Questions expose learners to a diversity of subject-related vocabulary.

8. The cards can assist intervention for those students who have had difficulty with numeracy assessments.

9. It can be a valuable practice to repeat a card some weeks later to enable students to consolidate concepts and promote learning from peers. Revision can also encourage confident participation from students who have gleaned knowledge from the discussions generated by previous sessions.

10. It is not necessary to address all 10 questions on each card in one session, or even in the given order.

2	5	10
0	1	6
3	7	4
6	9	8

CAN U questions

1. Can you find the biggest number on the card?

2. Can you find the smallest number on the card?

3. Can you find the numeral that is the same as the number of shoes you have on?

4. Can you find a numeral that shows how many doors there are in your classroom?

5. Can you find the numeral that is written twice on the card?

6. Can you find numerals that are written with only straight lines?

7. Can you find two numerals that have curved lines?

8. Can you find the number that begins with the *n* sound?

9. Can you find the smallest number on the top row?

10. Can you write two numbers on the card that are bigger than the number of fingers your teacher or partner is showing?

2	29	10
86	100	30
49	12	99
8	84	88

CAN U questions

1. Can you find a number that is one more than another number on the card?

2. Can you write the numbers on the card from smallest to biggest?

3. Can you find 3 numbers on the card that make a sequence of counting by twos?

4. Can you find numbers on the card with 8 in the ones place?

5. Can you find a number that you can add 4 to and find the answer also on the card?

6. Can you choose one of the numbers on the card and draw it grouped in two equal collections?

7. Can you regroup 30 using only tens?

8. Can you find two numbers and their total on the card?

9. Can you find the number on the card that is closest to 50?

10. Can you find numerals that have the same number of tens?

GREEN • CARD 2

2	4	1
3	8	4
9	3	7
6	2	1

CAN U questions

1. Can you find numbers that match on the card?

2. Can you see which number is missing on the card when you count to 10?

3. Can you see a column on the card in which all the numerals have curved shapes?

4. Can you see a row or column that has two numbers greater than 5?

5. Can you name three people and find the number on the card that matches that many?

6. Can you find numbers on the card less than 6?

7. Can you make each number on the card bigger by one?

8. Can you find the number on the card that matches the total of all your fingers? Do not count your thumbs.

9. Can you choose a number on the card and give that many claps?

10. Can you find a number on the card and suggest an animal that has this number of legs?

GREEN • CARD 3

1	4	20
9	11	8
19	7	2
12	15	10

GREEN · CARD 4

CAN U questions

1. Can you find numbers between 10 and 20 on the card?

2. Can you find a way of making 15 using other numbers on the card?

3. Can you make all the numbers in one row larger by 10?

4. Can you write 12 in tens and ones using plus and equals signs?

5. Can you find a number to use as a start and count by tens to 100 from that number?

6. Can you find a number on the card to write correctly as a word?

7. Can you sort the numbers on the card into odd and even numbers?

8. Can you find numbers and their doubles on the card?

9. Can you find a number that would be the same as another number on the card if you added one?

10. Can you find all the numbers on the card that you would say if you counted by fives from zero?

GREEN • CARD 4

2	2	4	
	1	6	6
7	5	6	3

CAN U questions

1. Can you find the number on the card that shows how many in the Mother Bear, Father Bear and Baby Bear family?

2. Can you choose a number from the card that shows how many people are in your family?

3. Can you match a picture to a number on the card?

4. Can you find the smallest number on the card?

5. Can you find the number to show how many ducks would be left if one bird flew away?

6. Can you say three numbers on the card out loud?

7. Can you whisper a curvy number on the card?

8. Can you sit quietly with others in your class and quickly make a group showing a number on the card?

9. Can you find the numbers shown the most times on the card?

10. Can you say the numbers that are missing from the card when you count to 10?

GREEN • CARD 5

PLATFORM 1

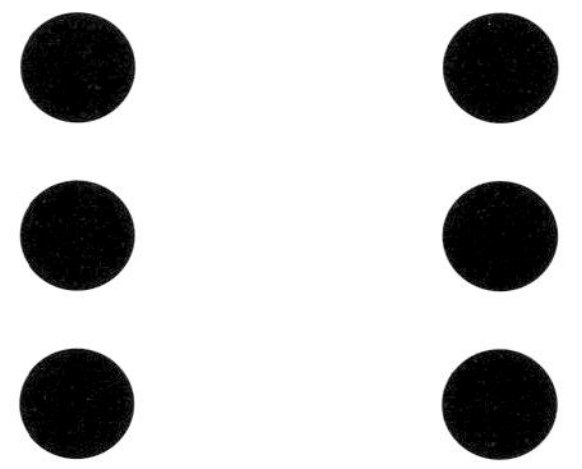	12	5
4	18	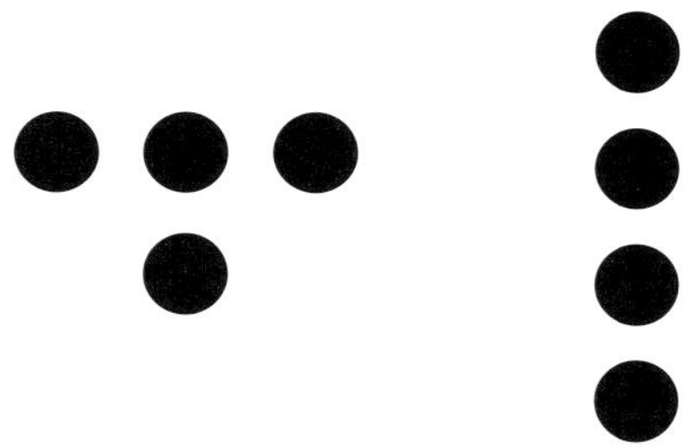
13	7	3
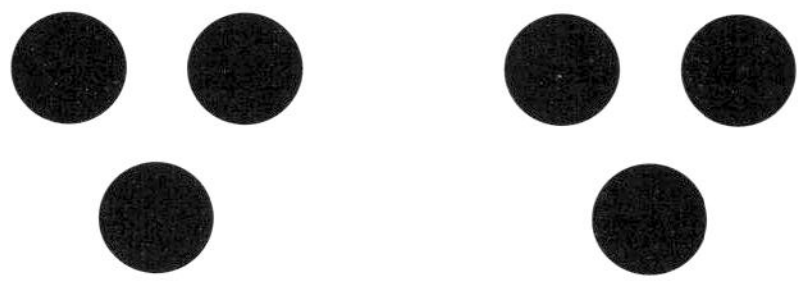	14	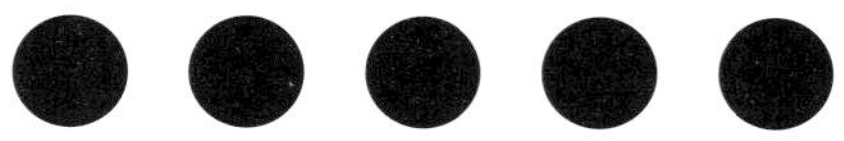

GREEN • CARD 6

CAN U questions

1. Can you find collections on the card shown in halves?

2. Can you find a numeral that matches a collection or half of a collection?

3. Can you find two collections of the same number on the card?

4. Can you find the smallest collection on the card?

5. Can you combine two collections on the card and find the number for the total on the card?

6. Can you write a number sequence, using numbers on the card, in which the numbers increase by one?

7. Can you sort the numbers shown in any form on the card into two groups – larger than 10 and smaller than 10?

8. Can you find the smallest number, shown in any form, in each row?

9. Can you find a number on the card to match this collection?

10. Can you draw a collection for a numeral on the card?

GREEN • CARD 6

PLATFORM 1

30	25	960
8	15	5
96	20	10
770	3	70

YELLOW · CARD 1

© TTS Group Ltd, 2012

CAN U questions

1. Can you find a number on the card that can be described as 900 + 60 + 0?

2. Can you find the numeral for 96 ones?

3. Can you find a number that has 7 in the tens place?

4. Can you find a number that is 10 more than another number on the card?

5. Can you find the number on the card that shows the total for seven hundreds and seven tens?

6. Can you make a multiplication number sentence using three numbers from the card (eg, 96 × 10 = 960)?

7. Can you find the number from the card that fits the missing number in this sequence? 10, 20, _____, 40

8. Can you find numbers on the card to fill in the missing numbers?
   15 + _____ = 30 – _____

9. Can you write all the odd numbers on the card that are smaller than 20?

10. Can you find a number and its double on the card?

YELLOW • CARD 1

20	100	55
120	17	90
22	15	2
4	13	11

CAN U questions

1. Can you see the number made up of 9 tens?

2. Can you start at a number on the card and count by fives to another number on the card?

3. Can you find numbers and their doubles on the card?

4. Can you find the numeral with the largest number of ones?

5. Can you find the numeral with the largest number in the ones place?

6. Can you find all the even numbers?

7. Can you find numerals where the tens place is empty?

8. Can you make a number sentence using numbers on the card so that the answer is the smallest number on the card?

9. Can you see numerals that have 2 in the tens place?

10. Can you see numerals that have the same number of tens and ones?

YELLOW • CARD 2

2	48	+
1	70	79
9	82	50
80	0	=

CAN U questions

1. Can you find the sign on the card that means *add*?

2. Can you find the best sign on the card to use to make a number less?

3. Can you count backwards by ones to show how you would get from 50 to 48?

4. Can you count forwards by tens to get from 9 to 79?

5. Can you choose a number from the card and regroup it in tens using the correct signs on the card?

6. Can you find a number on the card that has the same number of tens as another number on the card?

7. Can you write a number sentence using numbers on the card, two signs on the card and zero?

8. Can you find numbers on the card that would combine with a + sign to make 79?

9. Can you find a number on the card that you could make smaller by two and reach another number on the card?

10. Can you find a number with 8 in the tens place and a number with 8 in the ones place?

YELLOW • CARD 3

fifty

eighteen

sixty

eighty

10

50

ten

87

CAN U questions

1. Can you name the missing numbers on a number line on the card?

2. Can you place a number from the card onto a number line on the card?

3. Can you mark where 87 might fit on a number line on the card?

4. Can you find one number line that matches a part of another number line on the card?

5. Can you find words and numerals that match on the card?

6. Can you find a number line that leads you to 100?

7. Can you find a number on the card that is 7 more than eighty?

8. Can you find two words on the card that contain the same number word?

9. Can you write all the numbers (except the ones on the number lines) from largest to smallest?

10. Can you find the number on the card made by adding 5 groups of 10?

YELLOW • CARD 4

PLATFORM 1

36	4_9	⠿ (12 dots)
⠿ (9 dots)	9	17
6	30	(8 dots)
200	236	4

YELLOW · CARD 5

CAN U questions

1. Can you show which collection on the card is the largest?

2. Can you combine two collections on the card and find the total on the card?

3. Can you tell if all the collections would total more than 20? Explain how you can tell.

4. Can you choose a collection and show how you would group it in halves?

5. Can you find a collection that you could group in tens and ones?

6. Can you find a numeral on the card that shows how many tens fill the missing digit on the card to make four hundred and forty-nine?

7. Can you use at least three numbers on the card to make a number sentence?

8. Can you suggest a number on the card to fill the missing digit on the card to make that number larger than 459?

9. Can you write the number formed by combining 200 and 17?

10. Can you add the numbers represented on the card, including the collections, to make the closest number to 30?

YELLOW • CARD 5

14	29	81
3	39	55
19	↕	53
44	9	45

CAN U questions

1. Can you find numbers on the card that together would make a number made up of only tens?

2. Can you mark the number line to show how you could get to 9 in three hops?

3. Can you start with 9 and find three other numbers on the card to place in even spacing along the number line?

4. Can you find numbers on the card that you would say when counting by fives to 100 from 0?

5. Can you find two numbers on the card that differ by 11?

6. Can you find numbers on the card that differ by less than 3?

7. Can you find all the odd numbers on the card?

8. Can you round all the numbers to the nearest ten?

9. Can you find the number on the card that could be written as 10 + 10 + 10 + 10 + 4?

10. Can you represent a number on the card in halves?

YELLOW • CARD 6

110	thirty	34	37
7	6	9	25
27	thirteen	101	twelve

CAN U questions

1. Can you name the number at the end of the top row?

2. Can you find a number that has the same digits as 110?

3. Can you find the number on the card that shows the difference between 110 and 101?

4. Can you find a number on the card that added to its neighbour on the card totals another number on the card?

5. Can you write the numbers given in words from smallest to largest?

6. Can you find a number and its double on the card?

7. Can you find numbers with the same digit in the tens place?

8. Can you guess which column would have the smallest total by looking at the numbers?

9. Can you make a counting sequence using two numbers on the card and adding a third number of your own to the sequence?

10. Can you increase a number on the card by two and find the answer on the card?

YELLOW • CARD 7

add	2	=
seventy	minus	4
equals	–	76
74	≠	2

CAN U questions

1. Can you tell a number story using only words, numbers and/or symbols on the card?

2. Can you find signs or words on the card that are the same?

3. Can you find signs or words on the card that are opposites?

4. Can you read across the second row and say the answer?

5. Can you say if the number story across the bottom row is True or False?

6. Can you add three numbers on the card and find their total on the card?

7. Can you write which number shown on the card has the smallest number in the ones place?

8. Can you tell how to make 8 using the numbers on the card?

9. Can you find a word on the card that means "take away"?

10. Can you write your own number sentence using numbers on the card and the ≠ sign?

YELLOW • CARD 8

21	14	58
39	20	18
60	6	798
784	43	23

CAN U questions

1. Can you find all the numbers on the card that can be shared into three equal groups?

2. Can you make a numeral that has the same digits in the tens and ones places, by adding numbers on the card?

3. Can you find numbers on the card that can be rounded to 40?

4. Can you find numbers on the card that fall between 17 and 52?

5. Can you find the number on the card that is three times 13?

6. Can you use *greater than* signs to describe three sets of different numbers on the card?

7. Can you find the number on the card made by adding 3 to (five times 4)?

8. Can you subtract two numbers on the card and find the answer also on the card?

9. Can you find a starting number on the card and count by tens to a finishing number on the card?

10. Can you find a number on the card that is exactly divisible by 4 and by 5?

RED • CARD 1

PLATFORM 1

3	15	400
7	355	28
2	4	100
300	50	5

RED · CARD 2

40 © TTS Group Ltd, 2012

CAN U questions

1. Can you find a number on the card that is 500 less than 900?

2. Can you find the number on the card that rounds 368 to the nearest 100?

3. Can you find the total of adding double 3 and triple 3 on the card?

4. Can you write some *times* number sentences using only numbers from the card?

5. Can you write the largest numeral using three one-digit numbers on the card?

6. Can you find the numerals on the card that describe 355 in hundreds, tens and ones?

7. Can you draw a number line to show three numbers on the card correctly?

8. Can you find a number and its half on the card?

9. Can you write one less than each number on the card?

10. Can you increase each number on the card by 100?

RED • CARD 2

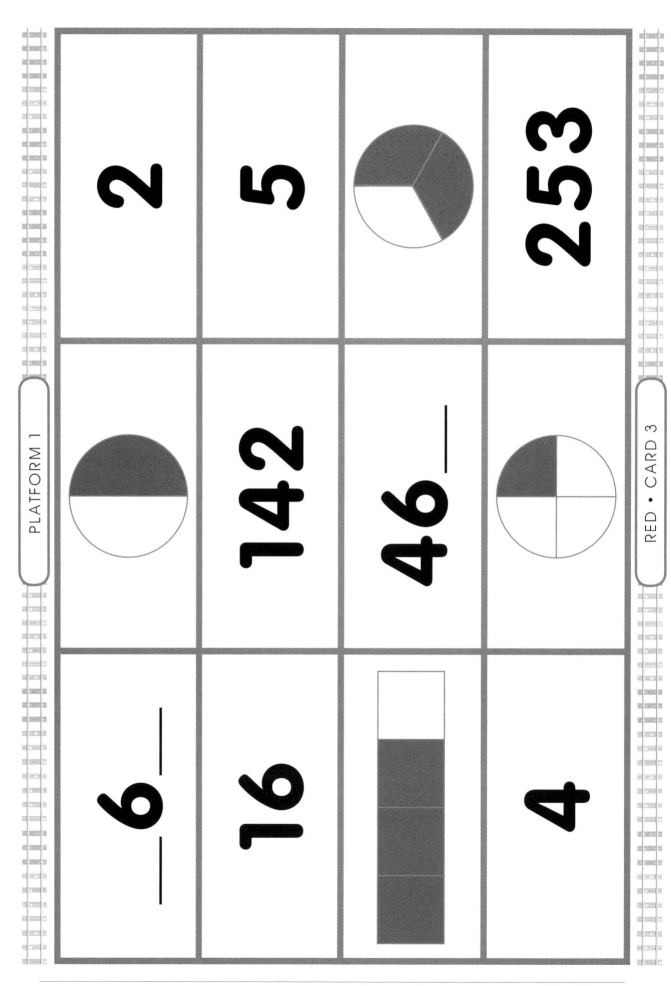

CAN U questions

1. Can you find the numbers on the card that fill the missing digits of a number on the card to make four hundred and sixty-two?

2. Can you use 462 and another number on the card to make a number sentence whose answer is 460?

3. Can you find a picture on the card with more than half shaded?

4. Can you find a picture on the card that shows a shape divided into quarters?

5. Can you find a shape on the card that would make one whole if you shaded one more piece?

6. Can you find a number on the card that could be shared equally in each section of the rectangle shape?

7. Can you use numbers on the card to complete this pattern? 2, ____ , 8, ____

8. Can you find numbers on the card whose digits, when compared, differ by one in each of the hundreds, tens and ones places?

9. Can you find a digit not used on this card?

10. Can you make 253 up to 260 adding numbers on the card?

RED • CARD 3

ten	6	2
~~IIII~~ III	1000	12
500	20	~~IIII~~ ~~IIII~~ ~~IIII~~
18	8	3

CAN U questions

1. Can you find the largest number to reach on the card if you counted by hundreds from zero?

2. Can you find tally marks that match numbers on the card?

3. Can you add all the tally marks and find the total on the card?

4. Can you write some *times* number sentences using only numbers shown on the card?

5. Can you find numbers to add from the card whose total is less than 20?

6. Can you find a way to make 40 from using numbers on the card?

7. Can you use the tally marks and numerals on the card to make number stories?

8. Can you double all the numbers on a row of the card?

9. Can you find the tally number on the card to double to make 16?

10. Can you find a way across the card (left to right) using neighbouring numbers that are only groups of 10? (You can move horizontally, vertically and diagonally.)

RED • CARD 4

241	85	59
>	686	121 + 121
3		72
242	=	

CAN U questions

1. Can you use your calculator to find three numbers on the card whose total is 1 000?

2. Can you show the circled part of the collection as a fraction?

3. Can you use a collection on the card and add it to two other numbers on the card to make a total shown on the card? (You can use your calculator.)

4. Can you find numbers (represented in any form) on the card that are shown in halves?

5. Can you write all the three-digit numbers on the card from largest to smallest?

6. Can you use a sign on the card to compare two numbers (represented in any form) on the card?

7. Can you find numerals on the card with an even number in the tens place?

8. Can you find a numeral on the card whose pattern of digits is the same forwards or backwards?

9. Can you find numbers on the card where one can be added or subtracted to reach the nearest ten?

10. Can you find a row of numbers (represented in any form) whose total will be closest to 85?

RED • CARD 5

999	1	5
<	=	646
4	2	12
6	>	352

CAN U questions

1. Can you round the three-digit numbers on the card to the nearest 10?

2. Can you use the addition of two numbers on the card to equal the subtraction of numbers on the card?

3. Can you find the three-digit number on the card that could be shared equally amongst 3?

4. Can you write a number that is half the value of a three-digit number on the card?

5. Can you show ways of making 6 using numbers from the card?

6. Can you regroup a three-digit number on the card into hundreds, tens and ones?

7. Can you write a number sentence for each of the signs on the card using numbers on the card?

8. Can you use only 999 and 1 to make a number sentence with < ?

9. Can you write a number sentence using the most two-digit and one-digit numbers on the card?

10. Can you suggest which number on the card would be closest to the number of days in a year?

RED • CARD 6

10	50	150
100	2	40
70	200	30
90	3	110

CAN U questions

1. Can you write in words two of the numbers on the card that are made up of tens only?

2. Can you find numbers on the card that differ by 10?

3. Can you find a way of crossing the card (top to bottom, left to right or diagonally), using only numbers that are multiples of 10?

4. Can you subtract a number on the card from another number on the card to make an answer that is an odd number?

5. Can you add two numbers on the card and find their total on the card?

6. Can you estimate the row on the card that would have the largest total? (Explain how you did this.)

7. Can you write a *times* number sentence using only numbers from the card?

8. Can you find ways of getting to 300 using the numbers on the card?

9. Can you make a number line to show three numbers on the card?

10. Can you estimate if all the three-digit numbers on the card would total more than 500?

RED • CARD 7

2	21	×
multiply	11	3
14	=	–
7	29	less

CAN U questions

1. Can you find signs and words on the card that have similar meanings?

2. Can you find a number and its factors on the card?

3. Can you find a number on the card to double in order to get an answer closest to 21?

4. Can you find numbers on the card that are doubles plus one?

5. Can you use at least two signs and numbers from the card to write a number sentence?

6. Can you choose which word you would use from the card to describe how to get 6 from two numbers on the card?

7. Can you find numbers on the card that could be rounded to 10?

8. Can you choose which word on the card you would use in describing how to make 10 from two numbers on the card?

9. Can you list the odd numbers on the card?

10. Can you add two numbers on the card and find their total on the card?

RED • CARD 8

Suggested answers

Green CAN U CARD 1 – Platform 1
1. 10
2. 0
3. 2
4. Answers may vary.
5. 6
6. 1, 4, 7
7. 0, 2, 3, 5, 6, 8, 9
8. 9
9. 2
10. Answers may vary.

Green CAN U CARD 2 – Platform 1
1. 30, 100
2. 2, 8, 10, 12, 29, 30, 49, 84, 86, 88, 99, 100
3. 8, 10, 12 or 84, 86, 88
4. 88, 8
5. 8 (+ 4 = 12), 84 (+ 4 = 88)
6. 10; Possible drawing:
   Also: 12, 2, 30, 8 etc.
7. 30 = 10 + 10 + 10
8. 2 + 8 = 10, 86 + 2 = 88, 88 + 12 = 100, etc.
9. 49
10. 10 and 12; 84, 86 and 88; (accept 2 and 8)

Green CAN U CARD 3 – Platform 1
1. 1/1, 2/2, 3/3, 4/4
2. 5 (accept 10)
3. 2, 3, 9, 6
4. **7**/3/**9**, 2/3/**9**/**6**
5. 3
6. 4, 3, 2, 1
7. 2/5/3, 5/9/4, 8/4/10, 2/3/7
8. 8
9. Answers may vary.
10. Answers may vary.

Green CAN U CARD 4 – Platform 1
1. 11, 12, 15, 19
2. 11 + 4, 8 + 7, 1 + 4 + 10, 20 – 4 – 1,
   double 7 + 1, etc.
3. 30/14/11, 18/21/19, 12/17/29, 20/25/22
4. 10 + 2 = 12, 10 + 1 + 1 = 12, 10 + 2 = 10 + 1 + 1
5. 20 or 10
6. Answers may vary.
7. odd: 1, 11, 9, 7, 19, 15 even: 4, 8, 2, 10, 12, 20
8. 1/2, 2/4, 4/8, 10/20
9. 19 (20), 11 (12), 7 (8), 10 (11), 1 (2), 8 (9)
10. 10, 15, 20

Green CAN U CARD 5 – Platform 1
1. 3
2. Answers may vary.
3. 5 ; 2
4. 1
5. 4
6. Answers may vary.
7. Answers may vary.
8. Answers may vary.
9. 6, 6, 6; 2, 2,
10. 8, 9, 10

Green CAN U CARD 6 – Platform 1
1.
2. 5/ , 4/ , 3/ or
3. and
4.
5. + = 12
   + = 14
   + =13
6. 3, 4, 5 or 12, 13, 14
7. larger: 12, 13, 14, 18
   smaller: 3, 4, 5, , , ,
   7, ,
8. 5, 4, 3,
9. 12
10. Answers may vary, eg, =4

Yellow CAN U CARD 1 – Platform 1
1. 960
2. 96
3. 70, 770
4. 15/5, 20/10, 25/15, 30/20
5. 770
6. 3 × 10 = 30, 3 × 5 = 15, etc.
7. 30
8. 15 + **5** =30 – **10** , 15 + **10** =30 – 5
9. 3, 5, 15
10. 10/20, 15/30

Yellow CAN U CARD 2 – Platform 1

1. 90
2. 55 to 90, 15 to 100, etc.
3. 2 and 4, 11 and 22
4. 120 ones
5. 17
6. 2, 4, 20, 22, 90, 100, 120
7. 100 (accept 2 and 4)
8. $17 - 15 = 2$, $15 - 13 = 2$, $22 - 20 = 2$, etc.
   Can accept division for extension $22 \div 11 = 2$
9. 20, 22, 120
10. 11, 55, 22, 100

Yellow CAN U CARD 3 – Platform 1

1. +
2. –
3. 50, 49, 48
4. 9, 19, 29, 39, 49, 59, 69, 79
5. $50 = 10 + 10 + 10 + 10 + 10$, Also: 70 and 80
6. 70/79, 80/82 also accept 2/9
7. $47 + 0 = 47$, $50 - 0 = 50$, etc.
8. $70 + 9$
9. 82/80, 50/48
10. 82, 80, 48

Yellow CAN U CARD 4 – Platform 1

1. 40, 50 or 5, 15, 25 or 92, 96 or 5, 10, 15
2. Answers may vary, eg,

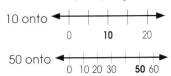

3.

4.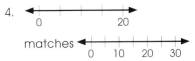

5. 10/ten, 50/fifty, 60/sixty
6.

86 88 90   94   98 100

7. 87
8. **eight**y and **eight**een
9. 87, eighty, sixty, fifty/50, eighteen, ten/10
10. 50/fifty

Yellow CAN U CARD 5 – Platform 1

1.
2. + = 17
3. Answers may vary.
4.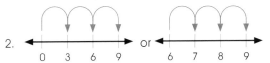
5.

6. 4
7. $4 \times 9 = 36$, $30 + 6 = 36$, $200 + 36 = 236$,
   $4 \times 9 - 30 = 6$, $36 - 6 = 30$, etc.
8. 6, 9
9. 217
10. $17 + 4 + 9 = 30$

Yellow CAN U CARD 6 – Platform 1

1. $81 + 9$, $45 + 14 + 81$, $55 + 45$, $14 + 3 + 53$, etc.
   (Discuss looking at ones house to achieve this.)
2.

0   3   6   9   or   6   7   8   9

3.

9 19 29 39

4. 45, 55
5. 55/44, 14/3
6. 45/44, 55/53
7. 81, 29, 55, 39, 3, 53, 19, 45, 9
8. 80, 30, 10, 60, 40, 10, 50, 20, 50, 10, 40
9. 44
10. $44 = 22 + 22$, $14 = 7 + 7$

Yellow CAN U CARD 7 – Platform 1

1. 110
2. 101
3. 9
4. $27 + 7 = 34$, $101 + 9 = 110$, twelve $+ 25 = 37$,
   $6 + 7 =$ thirteen, $9 + 25 = 34$ (neighbours can be vertical or horizontal)
5. twelve, thirteen, thirty
6. 6/twelve
7. 34/37, 25/27, 6/7/9, 13 thirteen/12 twelve/110
8. Middle column. Discuss why.
9. twelve, thirteen, **fourteen**; 6, 7, **8**; 7, 8, **9**;
   27, 37, **47**; 7, **17**, 27, etc.
10. 25/27, 7/9

Yellow CAN U CARD 8 – Platform 1

1. Answers may vary, eg, 74 minus 2 ≠ 76
2. equals/=, minus/−
3. add/minus, =/≠, add/−
4. 66
5. True
6. seventy + 4 + 2 = 76, seventy + 2 + 2 = 74
7. seventy
8. 2 + 4 + 2 = 8, 2 × 4 = 8, (76 + 2) − seventy = 8
9. minus
10. seventy ≠ 2, etc. Answers may vary.

Red CAN U CARD 1 – Platform 1

1. 21, 39, 18, 60, 6, 798
2. 66 (60 + 6, 43 + 23); 55 (21 + 14 + 20); etc.
3. 39, 43
4. 21, 39, 20, 18, 43, 23
5. 39
6. Answers may vary, eg, 798 > 784, 20 > 18, 23 > 6
7. 23
8. 798 − 784 = 14, 20 − 6 = 14, 43 − 23 = 20, etc.
9. Answers may vary, eg, 18 to 58 (possibly 798), 23 to 43, 20 to 60, possibly 14 to 784.
10. 20, 60

Red CAN U CARD 2 – Platform 1

1. 400
2. 400
3. 15
4. 5 × 3 = 15, 4 × 100 = 400, 2 × 50 = 100, etc.
5. 754
6. 300 + 50 + 5
7. Answers may vary. Discuss the variety.
8. 100/50, 4/2
9. 399, 14, 2, 27, 354, 6, 99, 3, 1, 4, 49, 299
10. 500, 115, 103, 128, 455, 107, 200, 104, 102, 105, 150, 400

Red CAN U CARD 3 – Platform 1

1. 4, 2 or 2
2. 462 − 2 = 460
3.
4.
5.

6. (may accept 2 broken into 4 halves)

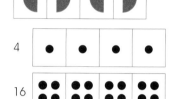

7. 4, 16
8. 253/142, 16/5
9. 0, 7, 8, 9
10. 253 + 5 + 2 = 260

Red CAN U CARD 4 – Platform 1

1. 1 000
2. 𝍸𝍸 and 10, 𝍸||| and 8
3. 18
4. 2 × ten = 20, 2 × 6 = 12, 3 × 6 = 18, 2 × 500 = 1 000, 6 × ten = 3 × 20, etc.
5. 3 + 6 + 2 = 11, 6 + 2 + 8 = 16, 𝍸||| + 3 + 2 = 13, etc.
6. 2 × 20, (3 × 20) − (2 × ten), ten + 20 + 𝍸𝍸, 18 + 2 + 20, etc.
7. 𝍸𝍸 + 𝍸||| = 18, 𝍸𝍸 = ten.   Explore minus, etc.
8. 4/12/twenty, 24/2 000/ or accept 16, 20 or 𝍸𝍸𝍸| or 𝍸𝍸𝍸𝍸 /40/1 000, 6/16/36
9. 𝍸|||
10. 𝍸𝍸 /20/1 000/ten
    𝍸𝍸 /20/500
    𝍸𝍸 /1 000/ten, etc.

Red CAN U CARD 5 – Platform 1

1. $686 + 242 + 72$
2. $\frac{1}{2}$, $\frac{5}{10}$
3. [dominoes] $+ 59 + 3 = 72$

   [dominoes] $+ 72 + 3 = 85$
4. [dominoes] , [dominoes] , $121 + 121$
5. 686, 242, 241
6. Answers may vary, eg, $686 > 121 + 121$
7. 241, 85, 686, 121, 242
8. 242, 686, 121
9. 241, 59, 121
10. $3 + 72 +$ [dominoes] $= 83$

Red CAN U CARD 6 – Platform 1

1. 350, 1 000, 650
2. $646 + 352 = 999 - 1$, $6 + 4 = 12 - 2$,
   $6 + 2 = 12 - 4$, etc.
3. 999
4. 323, 176
5. $5 + 1$, $2 + 4$, $12 - 6$, $12 - 5 - 1$, $12 - 4 - 2$,
   $5 + 4 - 2 - 1$, $(12 + 4) - (2 \times 5)$
6. $999 = 900 + 90 + 9$, $646 = 600 + 40 + 6$,
   $352 = 300 + 50 + 2$
7. $5 + 1 = 6$, $999 > 646$, $2 < 12$, etc.
   Answers may vary.
8. $999 - 1 < 999 + 1$, $1 < 999$
9. $12 + 2 = 6 + 4 + (5 - 1)$, $6 + 5 + 4 = 12 + 2 + 1$.
   Answers may vary.
10. 352

Red CAN U CARD 7 – Platform 1

1. fifty, forty, ninety, thirty, one hundred and
   ten, etc.
2. 100/90, 110/100, 40/30, 40/50
3. 40/200/90, 150/50/10, 110/200/100,
   30/200/70, 10/100/70/90, 150/40/30/110, etc.
4. Can only subtract 3 from all the numbers,
   except 2.
5. $70 + 40 = 110$, $50 + 40 = 90$, $30 + 40 = 70$,
   $100 + 50 = 150$, etc.
6. $30 + 200 + 70$. Discuss strategies.
7. $2 \times 100 = 200$, $3 \times 30 = 90$, $3 \times 50 = 150$, etc.
8. $200 + 100$, $200 + 70 + 30$, $150 + 50 + 100$,
   $110 + 90 + 100$, $(2 \times 30) + 40 + 200$, etc.
9. Answers may vary.
10. Yes. Discuss estimation strategies.

Red CAN U CARD 8 – Platform 1

1. ×/multiply, accept –/less
2. 21 factors 7 and 3, 14 factors 7 and 2
3. $11 \times 2 = 22$
4. 7, 29
5. Answers may vary, eg, $3 \times 7 = 21$, $29 - 7 = 2 \times 11$.
6. multiply (2 by 3)
7. 11, 14, 7
8. less, eg, 21 less $11 = 10$
9. 3, 7, 11, 21, 29
10. $14 + 7 = 21$, $11 + 3 = 14$

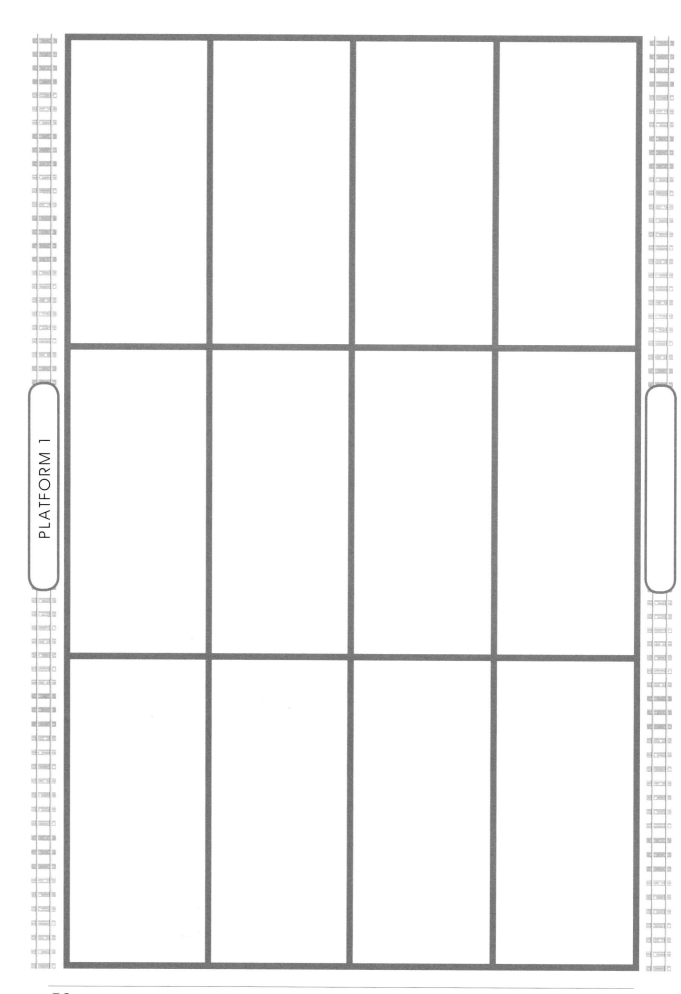

PLATFORM 1

PLATFORM
№ 1

Name: _____

Date: _____

Recording sheet

1. _____

2. _____

3. _____

4. _____

5. _____

6. _____

7. _____

8. _____

9. _____

10. _____

PLATFORM №1

Tracking sheet

Student	Green						Yellow								Red							
	1	2	3	4	5	6	1	2	3	4	5	6	7	8	1	2	3	4	5	6	7	8